Masterpieces

Addition and Subtraction

YEARS 3 AND 4

Contents

Contents

Coverage of National Numeracy Strategy "Framework"

Year 3 Objectives	Year 4 Objectives
Rapid recall of + and – facts	
• all addition and subtraction facts for each number to 20 • all pairs of multiples of 100 with a total of 1000 • all pairs of multiples of 5 with a total of 100	• addition and subtraction facts for all numbers to 20 • all number pairs that total 100 • all pairs of multiples of 50 with a total of 1000
Mental calculation strategies (+ and –)	
• count on or back • add several small numbers • partition into tens and units • find a small difference by counting up • identify near doubles • add and subtract mentally a near multiple of 10 • use known number facts and place value to add/subtract mentally	• find a small difference by counting up • count on or back • partition into tens and units • identify near doubles • add or subtract the nearest multiple of 10 • add several small numbers • use known number facts and place value to add/subtract mentally
Pencil-and-paper procedures	
• use informal pencil-and-paper methods • begin to use column addition and subtraction	• column addition and subtraction of two whole numbers less than 1000 • money calculations
Checking results	
• check with the inverse operation • repeat addition in a different order • check with an equivalent calculation	• check with the inverse operation • check with an equivalent calculation • estimate and check by approximating (round to nearest 10 or 100) • use knowledge of sums or differences of odd/even numbers

Diagnostic assessment

1 Write the answers in the boxes.

$2 + 7 = \boxed{}$ $8 + 6 = \boxed{}$ $5 + 9 = \boxed{}$

$9 - 4 = \boxed{}$ $11 - 5 = \boxed{}$ $14 - 3 = \boxed{}$

2 $25 + 75 = \boxed{}$ $35 + \boxed{} = 100$ $85 + \boxed{} = 100$

3 $300 + \boxed{} = 1000$ $600 + \boxed{} = 1000$

A Sheets

4 Write the answers in the boxes.

$11 + 9 = \boxed{}$ $12 + 5 = \boxed{}$ $13 + 9 = \boxed{}$

$14 - 6 = \boxed{}$ $17 - 8 = \boxed{}$ $18 - 9 = \boxed{}$

5 $65 + 35 = \boxed{}$ $36 + \boxed{} = 100$ $72 + \boxed{} = 100$

6 $350 + \boxed{} = 1000$ $550 + \boxed{} = 1000$

B Sheets

7 Write the answers in the boxes.

$16 + 15 = \boxed{}$ $17 + 14 = \boxed{}$ $18 + 19 = \boxed{}$

$17 - 9 = \boxed{}$ $15 - 8 = \boxed{}$ $19 - 14 = \boxed{}$

8 $42 + 58 = \boxed{}$ $29 + \boxed{} = 100$ $67 + \boxed{} = 100$

9 $1000 - \boxed{} = 400$ $1000 - \boxed{} = 250$

C Sheets

Recall of addition and subtraction facts to 20

1 Write the answers in the boats.

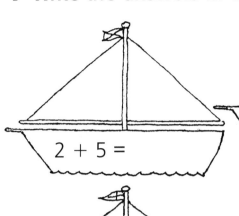

2 + 5 =

4 add 3 =

5 + 4 =

8 plus 6 =

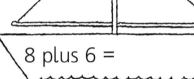

7 + 5 =

3 add 12 =

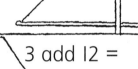

8 − 5 =

9 − 4 =

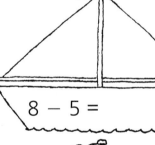

12 minus 7 =

13 take away 2 =

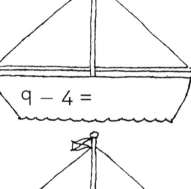

15 − 5 =

14 subtract 6 =

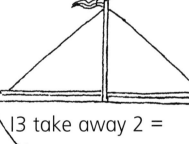

2 Do these quickly.

5 + 11 = ☐   10 − 6 = ☐   14 + 3 = ☐   12 − 4 = ☐

7 + 12 = ☐   16 − 6 = ☐   4 + 13 = ☐   15 − 4 = ☐

17 − 6 = ☐   20 − 10 = ☐   8 + 11 = ☐   13 + 5 = ☐

Recall of addition and subtraction facts to 20

1 Complete these addition grids.

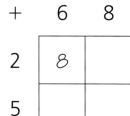
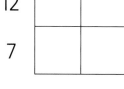

+	6	8
2	8	
5		

+	8	5
12		
7		

+	8	9
11		
7		

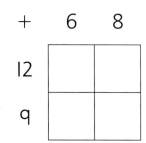
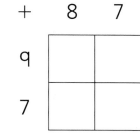

+	6	8
12		
9		

+	9	13
7		
5		

+	8	7
9		
7		

2 Now try these.

+		8
11	18	
		20

+	5	
	14	
14		20

+		
14	20	
12		17

3 Choose your own numbers for these.

+		

+		

+		

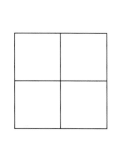
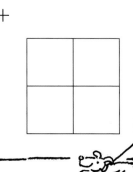

B *Masterpieces:* **Addition and Subtraction** ADDITION AND SUBTRACTION FACTS **YEARS 3/4**

Recall of addition and subtraction facts to 20

1 Complete these addition grids.

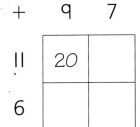
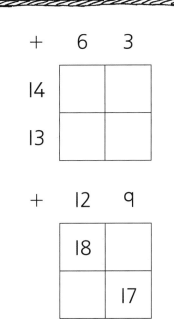

+	9	7
11	20	
6		

+	8	7
11		
12		

+	6	3
14		
13		

+	9	8
7		
9		

+		7
11	20	
		16

+	12	9
	18	
		17

2 Do these in the same way.

+	6	5	7
13			
9			

+	9	7	8
			19
	17		

+	5		
14	14		
12		20	19

3 Choose your own numbers for these.

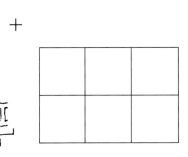
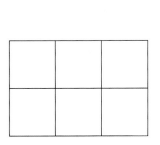
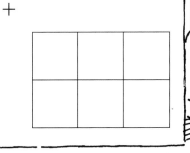

Name _____ Date _____

Pairs of multiples of 5 that total 100

1 Join each sock to a shoe to make 100.

2 100 − ⬚ = 65   45 + ⬚ = 100   100 − 85 = ⬚

   ⬚ + 75 = 100   100 − 40 = ⬚   ⬚ + 95 = 100

A *Masterpieces:* **Addition and Subtraction** ADDITION AND SUBTRACTION FACTS **YEARS 3/4**

Pairs of numbers that total 100

1 Write the number on the flag so that each pair totals 100.

2 Write some different pairs of numbers that make 100 on these flags.

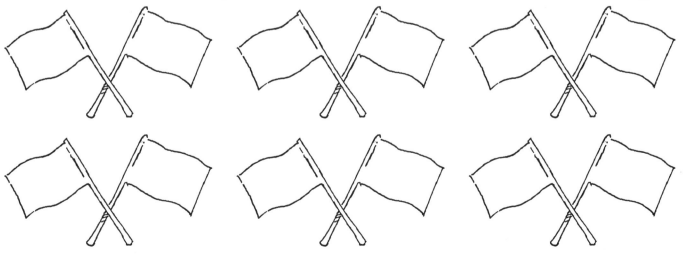

Name _____ Date _____

Pairs of numbers that total 100

1 Join pairs of things you could buy for exactly £1.

 27p

 38p

 58p

 64p

 39p

 61p

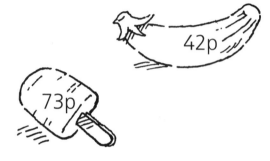 42p

 62p

 36p

73p

2 Write the number going into each pipe.

☐ 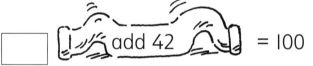 + 37 = 100   ☐ add 42 = 100

☐  plus 63 = 100

☐  + 19 = 100   ☐ + 78 = 100

☐ 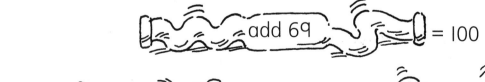 add 69 = 100

☐ 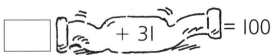 + 31 = 100   ☐ 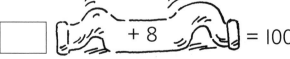 + 8 = 100

Pairs of multiples of 100 with a total of 1000

1 Each jar holds 1000 sweets. How many have been eaten?

300 [ ]

500 [ ]

400 [ ]

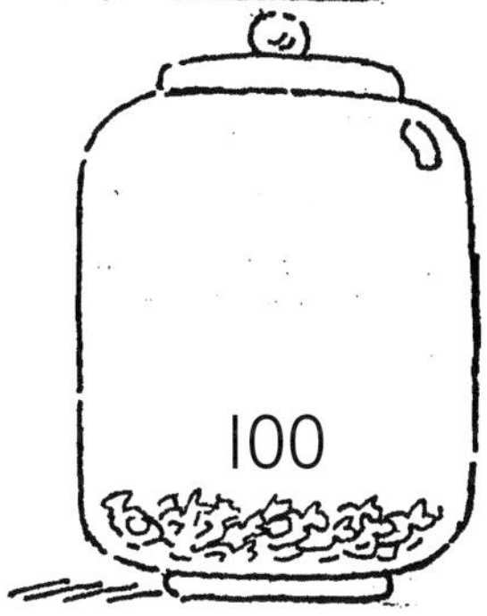

100 [ ]

800 [ ]

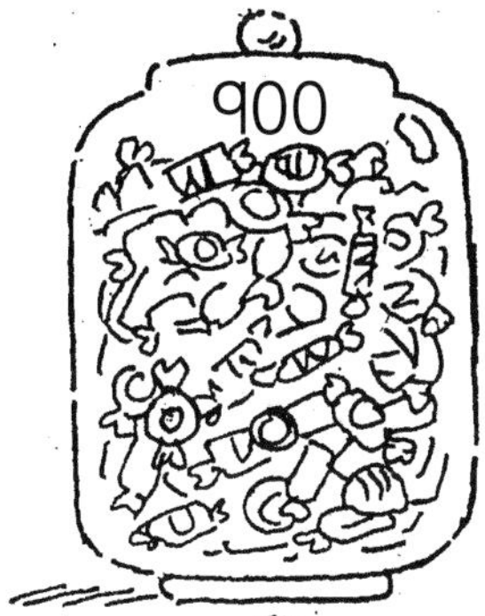

900 [ ]

600 [ ]

200 [ ]

700 [ ]

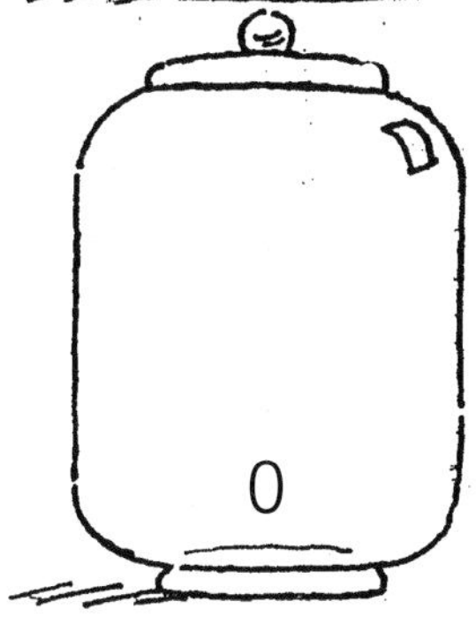

0 [ ]

Name _____ Date _____

Pairs of multiples of 50 with a total of 1000

1 Join pairs of numbers that add to 1000.

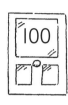 

 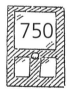 

2 Fill in the missing numbers.

400 + ☐ = 1000   200 + ☐ = 1000

300 + ☐ = 1000   700 + ☐ = 1000

600 + ☐ = 1000   150 + ☐ = 1000

Name _____ Date _____

Pairs of multiples of 50 with a total of 1000

1 Join pairs of things you could buy for exactly £1000.

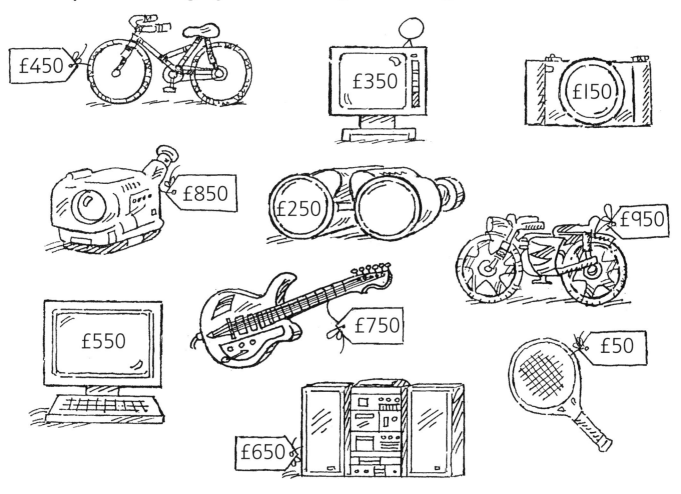

£450 £350 £150 £850 £250 £950 £550 £750 £50 £650

2 Write the missing numbers.

1000 less [   ] = 700

1000 − [   ] = 850

1000 minus 50 = [   ]

[   ] subtract 550 = 450

1000 − 650 = [   ]

1000 − [   ] = 350

1000 less [   ] = 750

1000 − 450 = [   ]

[   ] − 250 = 750

1000 subtract [   ] = 250

Name _____ Date _____

Diagnostic assessment

1 $8 + 1 =$ [ ] $15 + 10 =$ [ ] $37 - 10 =$ [ ]

2 $41 - 35 =$ [ ] $56 - 48 =$ [ ] $62 - 47 =$ [ ]

3 $5 + 8 + 3 =$ [ ] $7 + 4 + 9 =$ [ ] $4 + 8 + 1 + 7 =$ [ ]

4 $14 + 11 =$ [ ] $32 - 11 =$ [ ] $36 - 21 =$ [ ]

A
Sheets

5 $57 + 10 =$ [ ] $100 - 63 =$ [ ] $204 - 100 =$ [ ]

6 $138 - 27 =$ [ ] $154 - 32 =$ [ ] $145 - 29 =$ [ ]

7 $6 + 7 + 5 + 4 =$ [ ] $3 + 8 + 5 + 2 + 7 =$ [ ]

8 $25 + 9 =$ [ ] $42 + 19 =$ [ ] $37 - 19 =$ [ ]

B
Sheets

9 $78 + 100 =$ [ ] $1500 + 1000 =$ [ ] $3700 - 1000 =$ [ ]

10 $215 - 193 =$ [ ] $235 - 186 =$ [ ] $243 - 169 =$ [ ]

11 $60 + 70 + 20 =$ [ ] $70 + 50 + 30 =$ [ ]

12 $63 + 21 =$ [ ] $75 + 29 =$ [ ] $56 - 38 =$ [ ]

C
Sheets

Name _____ Date _____

Counting on or back in 10s or 1s

1 Write the answer at the end of each maze.

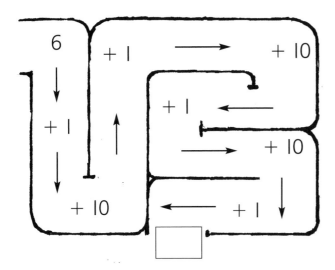

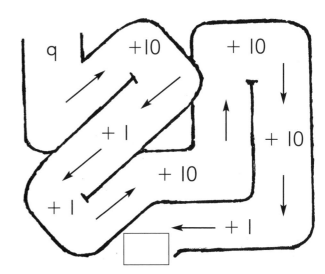

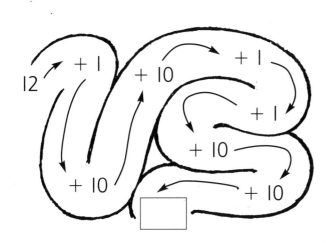

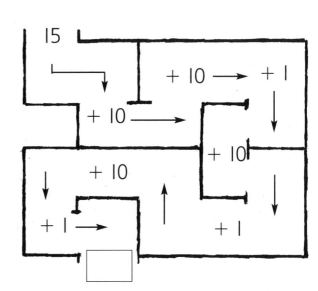

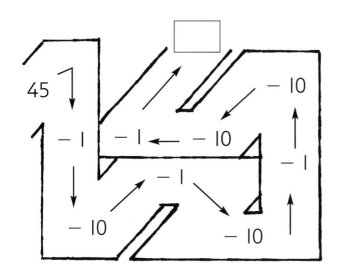

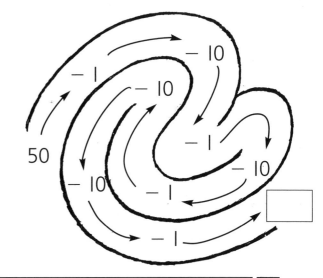

Name _____ Date _____

Counting on or back in 100s, 10s or 1s

1 Write the answer at the end of each maze and fill in the numbers as you go.

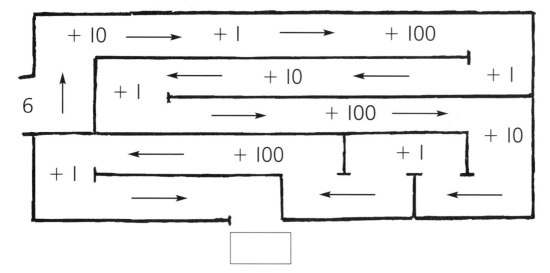

1	6
2	16
3	
4	
5	
6	
7	
8	
9	
10	
11	
12	

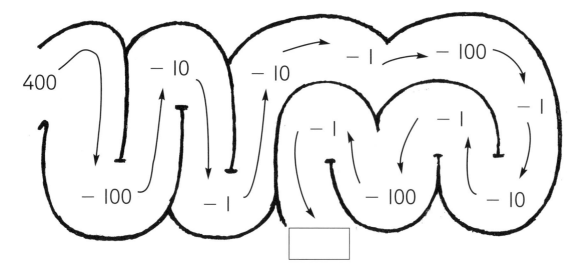

1	400
2	300
3	
4	
5	
6	
7	
8	
9	
10	
11	
12	

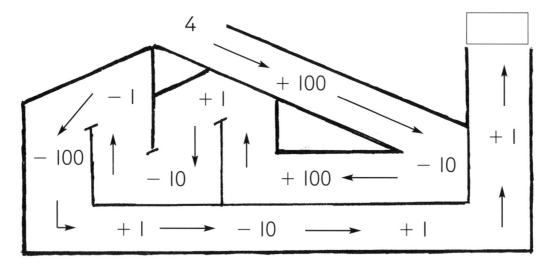

1	4
2	
3	
4	
5	
6	
7	
8	
9	
10	
11	
12	

B *Masterpieces:* **Addition and Subtraction** MENTAL CALCULATION STRATEGIES **YEARS 3/4**

Name _____ Date _____

Counting on or back in 1000s, 100s, 10s or 1s

1 Between each number in the maze, write down what is added or
subtracted. The first one has been done for you.

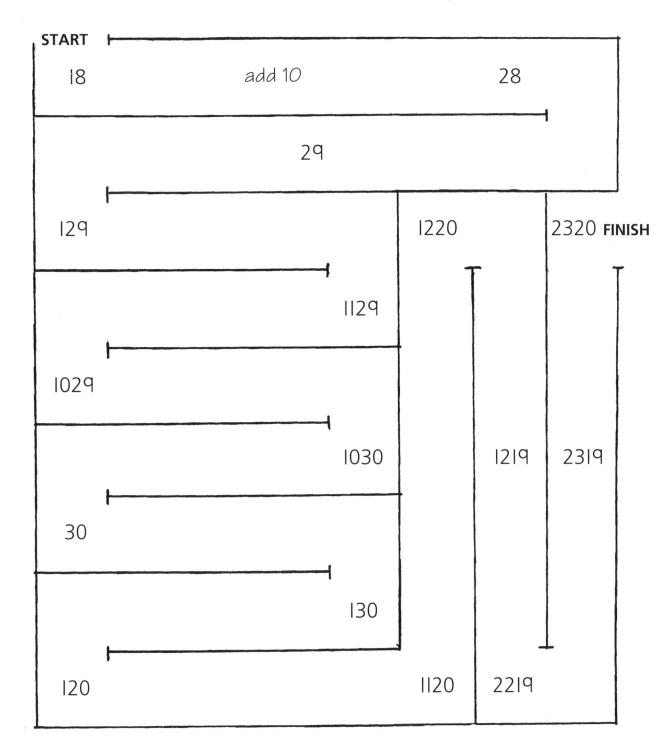

2 Choose a different start number and do the maze again.

Name _____ Date _____

Finding differences

1 Find the differences between these numbers by counting up.

Difference

66 − 59 $1 + 6 = 7$

```
   59   60           66
```

53 − 48 _____

```
   48                53
```

42 − 36 _____

62 − 52 _____

63 − 54 _____

71 − 63 _____

2 Now try these.

Difference

102 − 97 _____

```
   97                102
```

105 − 92 _____

108 − 99 _____

106 − 98 _____

104 − 92 _____

109 − 95 _____

Name _____ Date _____

Finding differences

1 Find the differences between these numbers by counting up.

109 − 96   **Difference**
                96   100   109   4 + 9 =

106 − 98   _____
                98   106

201 − 197   _____

304 − 298   _____

207 − 195   _____

403 − 394   _____

703 − 699   _____

807 − 794   _____

605 − 597   _____

901 − 895   _____

2 Try some more of your own.

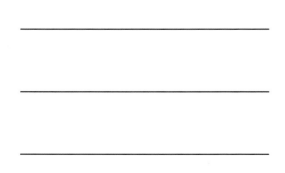

_____

_____

_____

Finding differences

1 Write the difference between the numbers in the box.

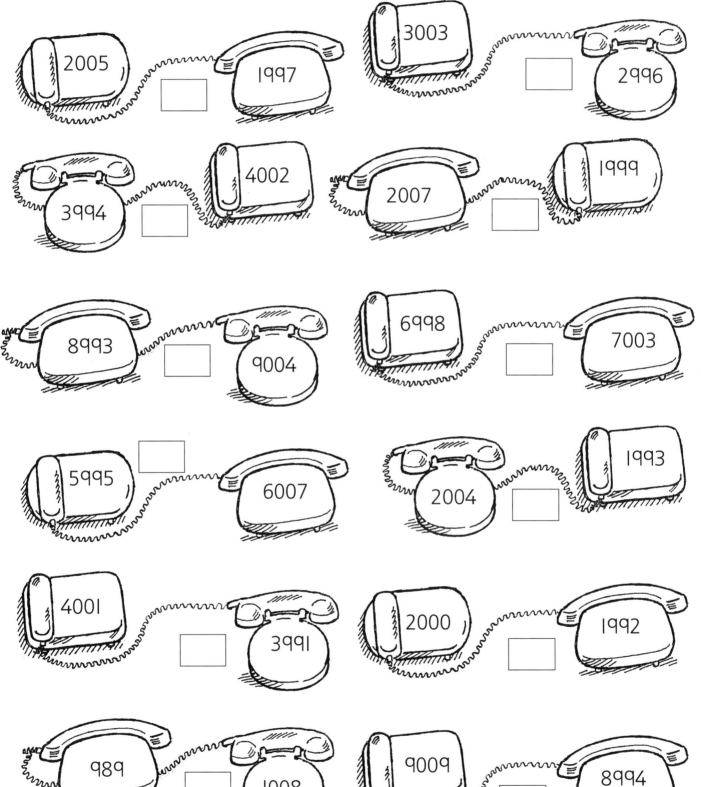

 C *Masterpieces:* **Addition and Subtraction** MENTAL CALCULATION STRATEGIES **YEARS 3/4**

Name _____ Date _____

Identifying near doubles using known doubles

1  Use doubles to answer these.

$$30 + 31 = 30 + 30 + 1 = 61$$

10 + 11 = ☐   20 + 21 = ☐   30 + 33 = ☐

40 + 41 = ☐   50 + 51 = ☐   50 + 52 = ☐

60 + 61 = ☐   70 + 71 = ☐   80 + 81 = ☐

40 + 43 = ☐   60 + 62 = ☐   70 + 73 = ☐

2
$$20 + 19 = 20 + 20 - 1 = 39$$

10 + 9 = ☐   30 + 29 = ☐   30 + 27 = ☐

40 + 39 = ☐   50 + 49 = ☐   60 + 59 = ☐

60 + 57 = ☐   70 + 69 = ☐   80 + 79 = ☐

70 + 67 = ☐   50 + 48 = ☐   80 + 77 = ☐

Name _____ Date _____

Identifying near doubles using known doubles

1 Join the boxes like the one shown.

50 + 60 =	70 + 70 + 10 =	150
90 + 80 =	50 + 50 + 10 =	170
70 + 80 =	130 + 130 − 10 =	310
100 + 110 =	90 + 90 − 10 =	110
130 + 120 =	180 + 180 − 10 =	250
150 + 160 =	150 + 150 + 10 =	210
180 + 170 =	100 + 100 + 10 =	490
190 + 180 =	250 + 250 − 10 =	730
250 + 240 =	190 + 190 − 10 =	370
360 + 370 =	360 + 360 + 10 =	350

2 Show how you work these out.

250 + 260 =

420 + 430 =

440 + 450 =

480 + 470 =

B *Masterpieces:* **Addition and Subtraction** MENTAL CALCULATION STRATEGIES   **YEARS 3/4**

Name _____ Date _____

Identifying near doubles using known doubles

1

Use doubles to answer these.

$$41 + 40 = 40 + 40 + 1 = 81$$

24 + 25 = ☐   18 + 19 = ☐   23 + 24 = ☐

32 + 33 = ☐   44 + 45 = ☐   27 + 28 = ☐

15 + 16 = ☐   38 + 37 = ☐   47 + 46 = ☐

35 + 36 = ☐   48 + 49 = ☐   26 + 27 = ☐

2

$$410 + 420 = 410 + 410 + 10 = 830$$

130 + 120 = ☐   250 + 240 = ☐   360 + 350 = ☐

170 + 160 = ☐   380 + 370 = ☐   490 + 480 = ☐

280 + 290 = ☐   440 + 430 = ☐   450 + 440 = ☐

260 + 270 = ☐   190 + 180 = ☐   470 + 480 = ☐

Name _____ Date _____

Adding several small numbers

Look for tens!

1 Add the numbers and
write the total in the box.

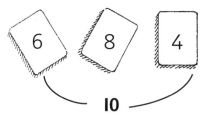

6 8 4 | 18 |

10

   ☐   ☐

8 7 2   5 7 3

 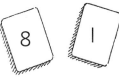 ☐   ☐

9 8 1   7 6 4

 ☐   2 4 5 8 ☐

3 5 7 2

  ☐

6 1 3 9 ☐   7 5 4 3

 ☐    ☐

5 6 4 1   7 8 5 2

 ☐    ☐

6 1 9 8   4 9 7 3

 ☐   ☐

15 3 6 5   5 8 17 3

23 6 7 5 ☐   ☐

6 9 21 8

A *Masterpieces:* **Addition and Subtraction** MENTAL CALCULATION STRATEGIES   **YEARS 3/4**

Name _____ Date _____

Adding several small numbers

1 Add the numbers and write the total in the box.

5	2	11	16	6
3	4	5	5	12
12	13	7	4	14
7	8	9	13	5

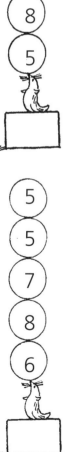

17	5	8	13	14
12	13	4	12	18
8	6	21	7	2
5	17	9	3	6

5	2	9	3	16
5	17	15	2	7
7	6	2	18	14
8	3	5	11	5
6	4	8	9	15

Name _____ Date _____

Adding three 2-digit multiples of 10

1 Write the total score next to each target.

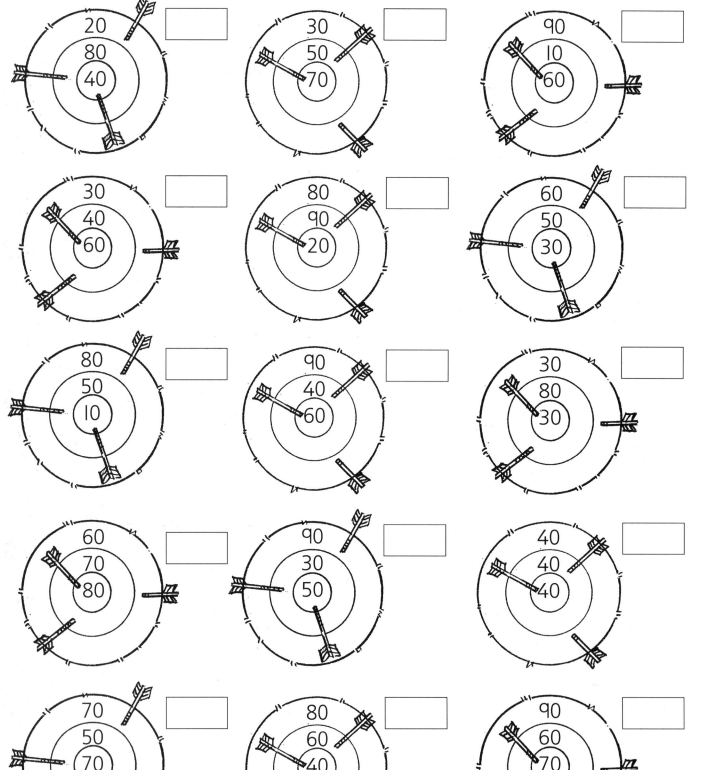

c *Masterpieces:* **Addition and Subtraction** MENTAL CALCULATION STRATEGIES   **YEARS 3/4**

Name _____ Date _____

Partitioning into tens and units: no exchange

1

Do these questions by "splitting up".

$25 + 14 = (20 + 10) + (5 + 4)$

$= 30 + 9$

$= 39$

$26 + 23 = (20 + 20) + (6 + 3)$

$=$

$=$

$27 + 32 = ($ $) + ($ $)$

$=$

$=$

$32 + 36 = ($ $) + ($ $)$

$=$

$=$

$45 + 33 =$

$=$

$=$

$47 + 22 =$

$=$

$=$

$41 + 54 =$

$=$

$=$

$43 + 56 =$

$=$

$=$

$39 + 60 =$

$=$

$=$

$54 + 35 =$

$=$

$23 + 51 =$

$=$

$=$

2 Make up some of your own.

Name _____ Date _____

Partitioning into tens and units: with exchange

1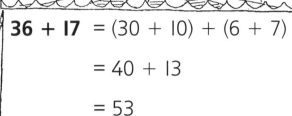
Do these questions by "splitting up".

$36 + 17 = (30 + 10) + (6 + 7)$

$\quad\quad\quad = 40 + 13$

$\quad\quad\quad = 53$

$35 + 27 = (\quad\quad\quad) + (\quad\quad\quad)$

$\quad\quad\quad =$

$\quad\quad\quad =$

$28 + 33 =$

$\quad\quad\quad =$

$\quad\quad\quad =$

$53 + 48 =$

$\quad\quad\quad =$

$\quad\quad\quad =$

$49 + 37 =$

$\quad\quad\quad =$

$\quad\quad\quad =$

$65 + 28 =$

$\quad\quad\quad =$

$\quad\quad\quad =$

$57 + 63 =$

$\quad\quad\quad =$

$\quad\quad\quad =$

$53 + 78 =$

$\quad\quad\quad =$

$\quad\quad\quad =$

$65 + 87 =$

$\quad\quad\quad =$

$\quad\quad\quad =$

$79 + 58 =$

$\quad\quad\quad =$

$\quad\quad\quad =$

Partitioning into hundreds, tens and units

1 You can do 143 + 36 like this⟶ 140 + 30 = 170
3 + 6 = 9 +
___
179

Do these in the same way.

127 + 42 ⟶ 120 + 40 =
7 + 2 =

146 + 23 ⟶

134 + 55 ⟶

157 + 38 ⟶

149 + 47 ⟶

154 + 39 ⟶

142 + 57 ⟶

158 + 42 ⟶

234 + 61 ⟶

287 + 96 ⟶

2 Write your own sums here.

Name _____ Date _____

Adding or subtracting 11 or 21

1 15 + 11 = ☐   17 add 11 = ☐   19 + 11 = ☐

24 + 11 = ☐   27 add 11 = ☐

28 + 11 = ☐   32 plus 11 = ☐   35 + 11 = ☐

36 add 21 = ☐   41 plus 21 = ☐

45 + 21 = ☐   49 + 21 = ☐

29 plus 21 = ☐

38 add 21 = ☐   47 + 21 = ☐

2 15 − 11 = ☐   24 minus 11 = ☐

19 − 11 = ☐

27 take 11 = ☐   34 subtract 21 = ☐

29 − 11 = ☐

37 less 21 = ☐   45 − 21 = ☐

38 minus 21 = ☐

49 − 21 = ☐   36 take away 21 = ☐

Adding or subtracting 9 or 19

1 $16 + 9 = \boxed{}$ $\qquad$ $32 + 9 = \boxed{}$ $\qquad$ $27 + 9 = \boxed{}$

24 add $9 = \boxed{}$

$46 + 9 = \boxed{}$ $\qquad$ 52 plus $9 = \boxed{}$

$22 + 19 = \boxed{}$

25 add $19 = \boxed{}$ $\qquad$ $31 + 19 = \boxed{}$

44 plus $19 = \boxed{}$

$37 + 19 = \boxed{}$ $\qquad$ 26 add $19 = \boxed{}$

2 $25 - 9 = \boxed{}$ $\qquad$ $31 - 9 = \boxed{}$

27 less $9 = \boxed{}$

43 take $9 = \boxed{}$ $\qquad$ 36 subtract $9 = \boxed{}$

34 minus $19 = \boxed{}$

36 subtract $19 = \boxed{}$ $\qquad$ $42 - 19 = \boxed{}$

$47 - \boxed{} = 19$

53 take away $\boxed{} = 19$ $\quad$ $64 - \boxed{} = 19$ $\qquad$ 76 subtract $\boxed{} = 19$

Name _____ Date _____

Adding or subtracting the nearest multiple of 10 and adjusting

1 36 + 9 = ☐   57 − 9 = ☐   27 minus 21 = ☐

47 add 11 = ☐

48 − 11 = ☐   64 plus 21 = ☐

42 + 19 = ☐

53 take 19 = ☐   63 + 29 = ☐

62 − 21 = ☐

74 add 31 = ☐   58 minus 31 = ☐

42 − 29 = ☐

66 + 39 = ☐   78 less 39 = ☐

75 plus 41 = ☐

2 61 + ☐ = 124   58 + ☐ = 100

93 take away ☐ = 59

170 − ☐ = 61   163 − ☐ = 89

79 add ☐ = 192   96 plus ☐ = 127

Masterpieces Ginn & Company 1999. Copying permitted for purchasing school only. This material is not copyright free.

Name _____ Date _____

Using known number facts and place value to add and subtract mentally

1 Join each key to the correct keyhole.

19   49

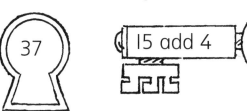

37   15 add 4

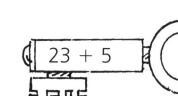

23 + 5

28

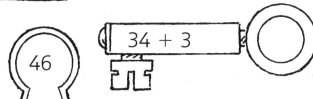

46   34 + 3

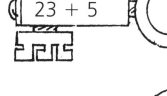

42 plus 7

59

40 add 6

54 + 5

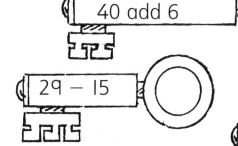

29 − 15

37 take away 16

142

16

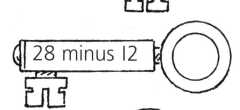

28 minus 12

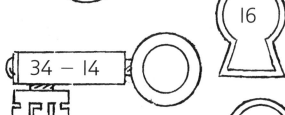

34 − 14

124 + 5

131 add 8

21

20

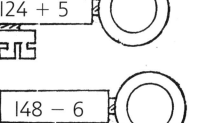

148 − 6

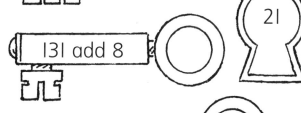

159 subtract 8

14   129

139   151

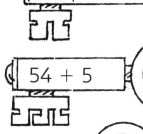

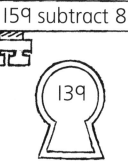

Name _____ Date _____

Using known number facts and place value to add and subtract mentally

1 Join each car to the correct garage.

 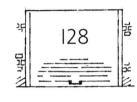  

   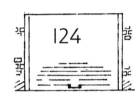

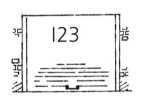   

Using known number facts and place value to add and subtract mentally

1 Write the answers in the boxes.

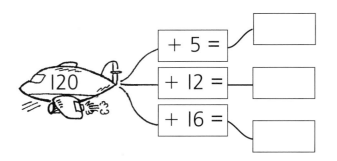

120

+ 5 = ☐

+ 12 = ☐

+ 16 = ☐

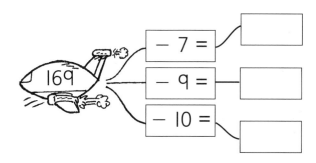

169

− 7 = ☐

− 9 = ☐

− 10 = ☐

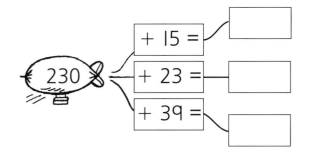

230

+ 15 = ☐

+ 23 = ☐

+ 39 = ☐

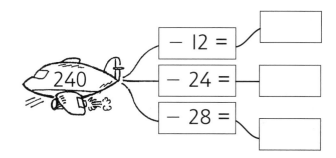

240

− 12 = ☐

− 24 = ☐

− 28 = ☐

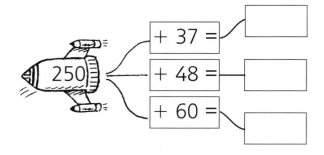

250

+ 37 = ☐

+ 48 = ☐

+ 60 = ☐

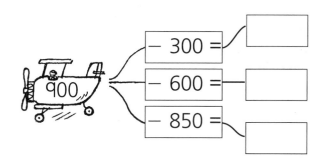

900

− 300 = ☐

− 600 = ☐

− 850 = ☐

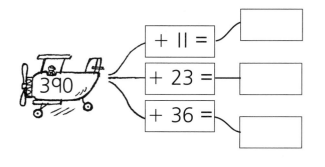

390

+ 11 = ☐

+ 23 = ☐

+ 36 = ☐

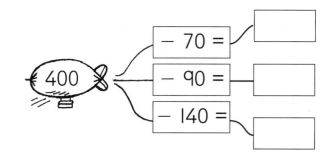

400

− 70 = ☐

− 90 = ☐

− 140 = ☐

Name _____ Date _____

Diagnostic assessment

1
```
  46          54         137
+ 23        + 35        + 42
____        ____        ____
```

2
```
 163         265         649
-  42        - 34        - 23
____        ____        ____
```

A Sheets

3 85 people went to the zoo. 42 were children.

How many were adults? ☐

4
```
 135         162         257
+  46        + 54        + 138
____        ____        _____
```

5
```
 141         325         548
-  26        - 74        - 69
____        ____        ____
```

B Sheets

6 Mr Wood had 153 books. Cathy bought 46.

How many does Mr Wood have now? ☐

7
```
 245         368         459
+ 176       + 154       + 273
____        ____        ____
```

8
```
 341         317         540
- 256       - 279       - 362
____        ____        ____
```

C Sheets

9 367 people went to the pool today. That's 184 more than yesterday.

How many went yesterday? ☐

Name _____ Date _____

Beginning to use column addition
(TU + TU, HTU + TU: exchange once)

```
  27
+ 38
-----
  50
  15
-----
  65
```

```
  27
+ 38
-----
  65
   1
```

You can do the same sum in different ways.

1 Choose which way to do these sums.

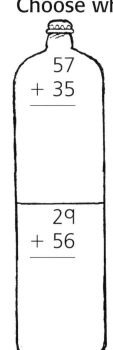

```
  57
+ 35
```

```
  29
+ 56
```

```
  45
+ 28
```

```
  62
+ 45
```

```
  52
+ 67
```

```
  54
+ 37
```

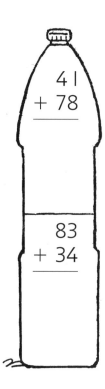

```
  41
+ 78
```

```
  83
+ 34
```

2 Now try these.

```
  125
+  67
```

```
  138
+  81
```

```
  132
+  29
```

```
  150
+  79
```

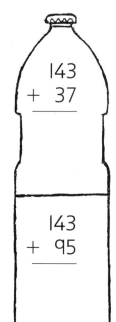

```
  143
+  37
```

```
  143
+  95
```

```
  155
+  26
```

```
  164
+  62
```

Using column addition
(HTU + TU, HTU + HTU: exchange once)

1 Do these sums and then colour in the answers in the box.
When you have finished, the whole box should be coloured.

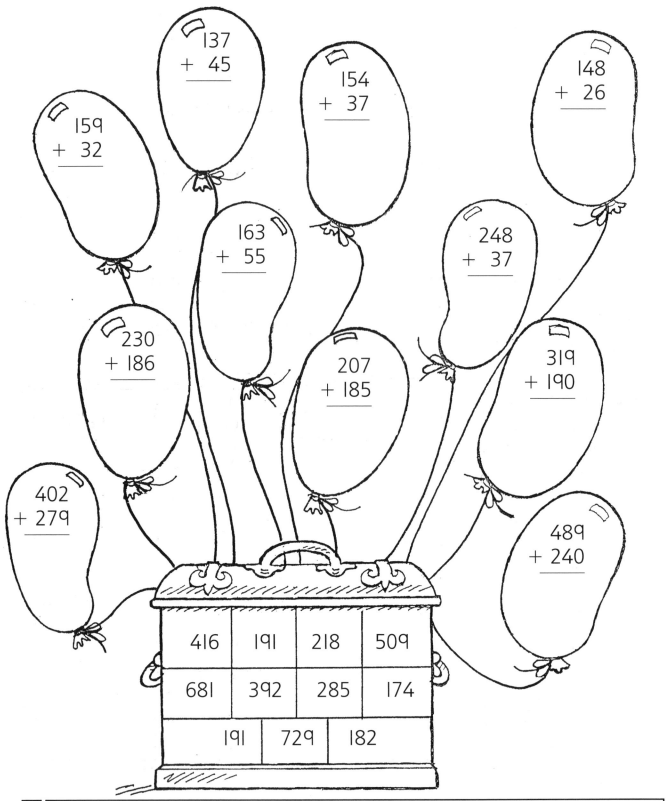

416	191	218	509
681	392	285	174

191	729	182

Name _____ Date _____

Using column addition (HTU + HTU: exchange twice)

1 Find the total mass of each parcel.

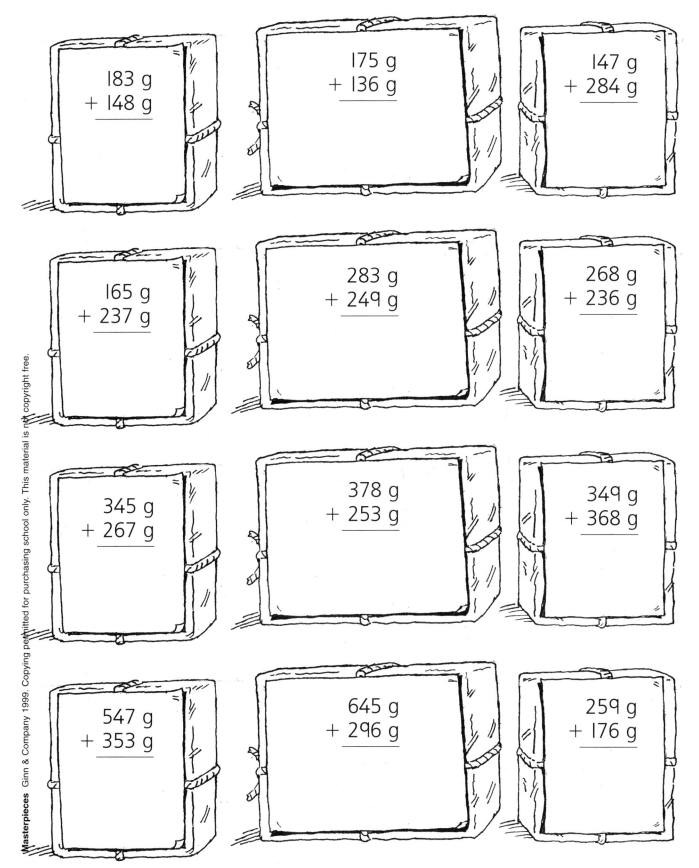

183 g
+ 148 g

175 g
+ 136 g

147 g
+ 284 g

165 g
+ 237 g

283 g
+ 249 g

268 g
+ 236 g

345 g
+ 267 g

378 g
+ 253 g

349 g
+ 368 g

547 g
+ 353 g

645 g
+ 296 g

259 g
+ 176 g

Name _____ Date _____

Beginning to use column subtraction
(HTU − TU: no exchange)

1 Use these numbers to answer the questions below.
Show your working.

786   51   278   23   869   15   24

☆ − ✏️ =   ✈️ − ✂️ =   ✔️ − ✏️ =

➡️ − ✔️ =   ✈️ − ♣️ =   ☆ − ✂️ =

☆ − ♣️ =   ✈️ − ✏️ =   ✔️ − ♣️ =

✔️ − ✂️ =   ☆ − ➡️ =   ✈️ − ✔️ =

2 Make up some questions of your own.

Name _____ Date _____

Using column subtraction (HTU − TU: with exchange)

1 Answer these questions. Colour the answers on the grid below.

$$142 - 25$$

$$287 - 48$$

$$483 - 34$$

$$392 - 64$$

$$845 - 83$$

$$547 - 66$$

$$753 - 70$$

$$605 - 43$$

$$342 - 78$$

$$460 - 85$$

$$704 - 46$$

$$506 - 59$$

107	123	240	842	117	742	425	336	300
120	762	683	848	481	521	306	449	375
241	249	451	723	501	614	400	405	702
264	658	450	703	239	642	700	328	562
329	330	332	602	447	552	742	503	553

What word does this show?

Name _____ Date _____

Using column subtraction (HTU − HTU: with exchange)

1 Use these numbers to answer the questions below.
Show your working.

732   679   243   803   357   158   650

🖊 − ☆ =	✈ − ✂ =	✂ − ✔ =
✔ − ➡ =	🖊 − ✂ =	✈ − ☆ =
✈ − ➡ =	✈ − ♣ =	➡ − ♣ =
☆ − ♣ =	🖊 − ✔ =	✔ − ☆ =
✔ − ♣ =	🖊 − ➡ =	🖊 − ✈ =

2 Make up some questions of your own.

Name _____ Date _____

Addition and subtraction in context
(TU ± TU, HTU ± TU: no exchange)

Answer these questions about the school fair.

1 The cost to enter the fair was 20p for children and 50p for adults. How much did it cost for John and his Dad to get in? ▭

2 John won some sweets on a stall and gave 8 of them away to his friends. He had 4 sweets left. How many did he win? ▭

3 12 girls and 15 boys took part in the sack race. What was the total number of children? ▭

4 On the hoopla, Sarah threw a hoop onto the numbers 15, 9 and 6. What was her total score? ▭

5 187 people went to the fair. 74 were adults. How many were children? ▭

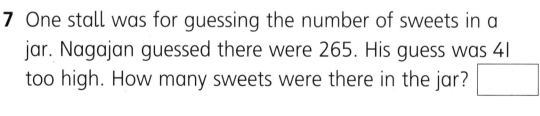

6 Ahmed had £1.85. He spent 65p on a hot dog. How much did he have to buy a drink? ▭

7 One stall was for guessing the number of sweets in a jar. Nagajan guessed there were 265. His guess was 41 too high. How many sweets were there in the jar? ▭

8 Josh's guess was 34 higher than Nagajan's guess. How many did Josh think were in the jar? ▭

9 187 people went to the fair. 92 people left before 3 o'clock. How many were still there after 3 o'clock? ▭

Name _____ Date _____

Addition and subtraction in context
(HTU ± TU: with exchange)

Answer these questions about the car boot sale.

1 In the morning there were 128 cars at the sale. 63 cars had things to sell. How many had nothing to sell? ☐

2 In the afternoon 57 more cars arrived.
How many cars were there in total? ☐

3 Mr Taylor was selling 176 crayons. Molly bought 38.
How many were left? ☐

4 Mrs Patel had 135 comics. Jack bought 62.
How many did she have left? ☐

5 Mrs Jones had 57 cups and 163 saucers.
How many more saucers than cups were there? ☐

6 What was the total number of cups and saucers? ☐

7 The ice cream van sold 154 ice creams in the morning and 73 in the afternoon. How many did it sell in total? ☐

8 307 people went to the sale. 86 people left before 2 o'clock. How many were still there after 2 o'clock? ☐

9 Molly had a £5 note. She spent 95p on crayons.
How much change did she get? ☐

10 There were 307 people at the sale.
Last week there were 96 more people.
How many people went to the sale last week? ☐

Masterpieces Ginn & Company 1999. Copying permitted for purchasing school only. This material is not copyright free.

Name _____ Date _____

Addition and subtraction in context
(HTU ± TU: with exchange)

Answer these questions about the cinema.

1 It cost £2.76 each for children to go to the cinema.
How much did it cost for 2 children? [ ]

2 It cost £4.68 each for adults to get in.
How much did it cost for 2 adults? [ ]

3 Jenny had a £5 note. She spent £1.75 on popcorn.
How much change did she get? [ ]

4 On the bus to the cinema, Jeremy and Jenny each
paid £1.68. How much did they pay in total? [ ]

5 There are 500 seats in the cinema. If there are 267
people, how many seats are empty? [ ]

6 Yesterday the cinema sold 168 ice creams. Today it
sold 249. How many were sold in the 2 days? [ ]

7 384 people went to the cinema.

a) This was 196 more than yesterday.
How many went to the cinema yesterday? [ ]

b) 295 were adults. How many were children? [ ]

c) 278 people were there at the start of the film.
How many were late? [ ]

Name _____ Date _____

Diagnostic assessment

1 Check these answers. Put a cross next to any that are wrong.

```
    186         243          167          258
  +  51       +  54        -  43        -  37
  ─────       ─────        ─────        ─────
    235         297          124          295
```

A
Sheets

2 Write 3 addition questions with these numbers: 5   2   4

+ + =		+ + =		+ + =

3 Check these answers. Put a cross next to any that are wrong.

```
    324         412          436          567
  + 169       + 296        - 132        - 259
  ─────       ─────        ─────        ─────
    493         708          314          312
```

4 Write 3 addition questions with these numbers: 9   12   16

+ + =		+ + =		+ + =

B
Sheets

5 Join these numbers to the nearest 10.

```
          64        78        93        108
```

(50)   (60)   (70)   (80)   (90)   (100)   (110)

6 Check these answers. Put a cross next to any that are wrong.

```
    586         492          425          605
  + 367       + 438        - 359        - 178
  ─────       ─────        ─────        ─────
    963         920           56          503
```

7 Write 3 addition questions with these numbers: 18   20   21

+ + =		+ + =		+ + =

C
Sheets

8 Join these numbers to the nearest 100.

```
          195        238        449        670
```

(100)   (200)   (300)   (400)   (500)   (600)   (700)

Checking with the inverse operation

1 Check these answers by <u>adding</u>. Correct any that are wrong.

```
      182              289              484
    -  51            -  48            -  62
    ─────            ─────            ─────
      131              241              422
Check:
    +  51
```

```
      895              589              790
    -  83            -  66            -  63
    ─────            ─────            ─────
      812              523              730
```

2 Check these answers by <u>subtracting</u>. Correct any that are wrong.

```
      326              231              434
    +  71            +  48            +  62
    ─────            ─────            ─────
      397              279              496
Check:
    -  71
```

```
      825              524              790
    +  73            +  66            +  63
    ─────            ─────            ─────
      858              590              853
```

Name _____ Date _____

Checking with the inverse operation

1 Do these addition questions and check your answers as shown.

436 + 132 =   **343 + 155 =**   **427 + 361 =**

436 + 32 = ⟶ ⟩ 568

436 = 132 − ⟵

Check

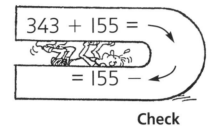

Check

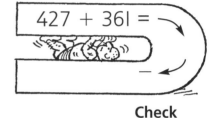

Check

528 + 221 =   **264 + 135 =**   **356 + 204 =**

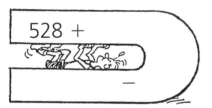

Check

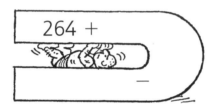

Check

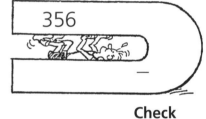

Check

2 Check these subtraction questions by adding.

565 − 326 =   **484 − 234 =**

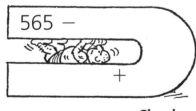

Check

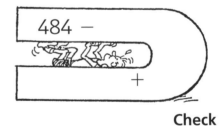

Check

638 − 423 =   **782 − 381 =**

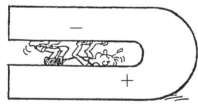

Check

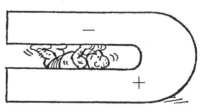

Check

Name _____ Date _____

Checking with the inverse operation

1 Write the missing numbers.

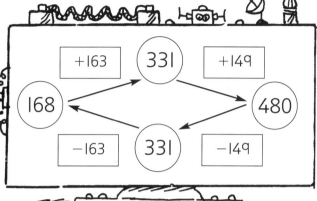

168 → +163 → 331 → +149 → 480
168 ← −163 ← 331 ← −149 ← 480

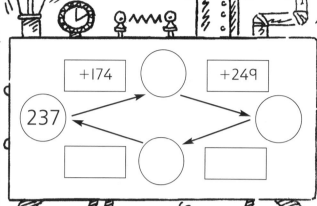

237 → +174 → ◯ → +249 → ◯

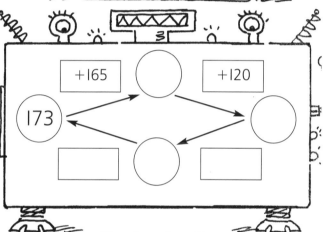

173 → +165 → ◯ → +120 → ◯

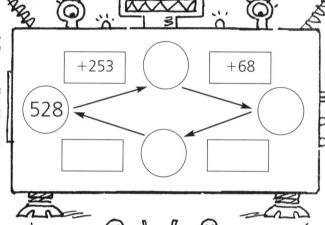

528 → +253 → ◯ → +68 → ◯

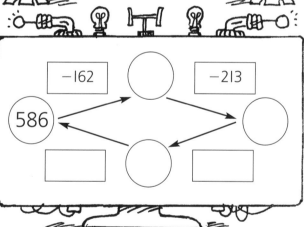

586 → −162 → ◯ → −213 → ◯

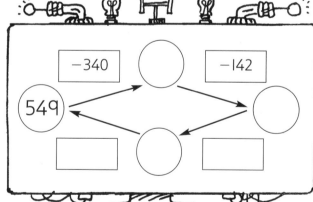

549 → −340 → ◯ → −142 → ◯

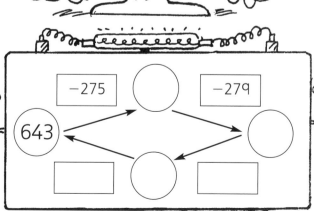

643 → −275 → ◯ → −279 → ◯

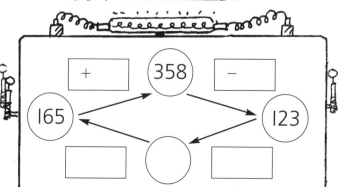

165 → + → 358 → − → 123

Name _____ Date _____

Repeating addition in a different order

Draw a loop to show which addition you work out first.
Show another way. Circle the way you think is easiest.

1st way	2nd way

8 + 4 + 2 = 14   8 + 4 + 2 = 14

1   2 + 8 + 5 =   2 + 8 + 5 =

2   3 + 4 + 7 =   3 + 4 + 7 =

3   9 + 4 + 6 =   9 + 4 + 6 =

4   6 + 1 + 9 =   6 + 1 + 9 =

5   5 + 10 + 5 =   5 + 10 + 5 =

6   8 + 5 + 2 =   8 + 5 + 2 =

7   8 + 5 + 5 =   8 + 5 + 5 =

Choose your own numbers for these.

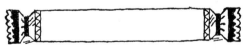

A   *Masterpieces:* **Addition and Subtraction** CHECKING RESULTS   YEARS 3/4

Name _____ Date _____

Repeating addition in a different order

Draw a loop to show which addition you work out first.
Show another way. Circle the way you think is easiest.

1st way	**2nd way**

6 + 9 + 4 = 19   6 + 9 + 4 = 19

1 7 + 3 + 8 =   7 + 3 + 8 =

2 8 + 9 + 1 =   8 + 9 + 1 =

3 12 + 7 + 3 =   12 + 7 + 3 =

4 3 + 16 + 4 =   3 + 16 + 4 =

5 15 + 9 + 5 =   15 + 9 + 5 =

6 10 + 17 + 3 =   10 + 17 + 3 =

7 9 + 12 + 11 =   9 + 12 + 11 =

Choose your own numbers for these.

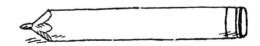

Name _____ Date _____

Repeating addition in a different order

Draw a loop to show which addition you work out first.
Show another way. Circle the way you think is easiest.

	Ist way	**2nd way**
	$16 + 7 + 4 = 27$	$16 + 7 + 4 = 27$
1	$13 + 7 + 8 =$	$13 + 7 + 8 =$
2	$14 + 15 + 6 =$	$14 + 15 + 6 =$
3	$12 + 16 + 8 =$	$12 + 16 + 8 =$
4	$20 + 50 + 80 =$	$20 + 50 + 80 =$
5	$60 + 40 + 70 =$	$60 + 40 + 70 =$
6	$90 + 80 + 20 =$	$90 + 80 + 20 =$
7	$70 + 90 + 30 =$	$70 + 90 + 30 =$

Choose your own numbers for these.

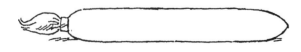

 C *Masterpieces:* **Addition and Subtraction** CHECKING RESULTS   YEARS 3/4

Masterpieces Ginn & Company 1999. Copying permitted for purchasing school only. This material is not copyright free.

Name _____ Date _____

Checking by approximating (rounding to the nearest 10)

1 This is Jonny's homework.
  Write an approximate answer for each question to help him.

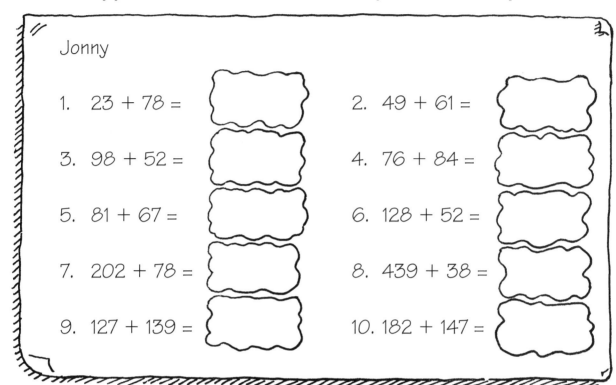

Jonny

1. 23 + 78 =

2. 49 + 61 =

3. 98 + 52 =

4. 76 + 84 =

5. 81 + 67 =

6. 128 + 52 =

7. 202 + 78 =

8. 439 + 38 =

9. 127 + 139 =

10. 182 + 147 =

2 Write the approximate differences between these numbers.

Difference   **Difference**

79	51		161	42
92	138		187	59
372	38		368	42
69	512		471	178
289	161		577	159
492	238		258	121

Name _____ Date _____

Checking by approximating
(rounding to the nearest 10 or 100)

This is Jason's homework.

Write an approximate answer for each question to help him.

Jason

1. 99 + 97 =

2. 89 + 71 =

3. 202 + 105 =

4. 209 + 203 =

5. 301 + 298 =

6. 319 + 322 =

7. 307 + 309 =

8. 397 + 404 =

9. 407 + 342 =

10. 639 + 158 =

11. 88 − 42 =

12. 97 − 61 =

13. 103 − 51 =

14. 199 − 31 =

15. 302 − 198 =

16. 597 − 302 =

17. 679 − 161 =

18. 883 − 397 =

19. 568 − 292 =

20. 961 − 182 =

Name _____ Date _____

Checking by approximating
(rounding to the nearest 10 or 100)

1 This toy shop has 2 floors.
There are 198 toys on the first floor and
304 on the second floor. About
how many toys are in the shop? [   ]

2 About how many toys are in these shops?

| SUPER TOYS | 148 toys on the first floor and 203 on the second floor | [   ] |

| Toy City | 208 toys on the first floor and 190 on the second floor | [   ] |

| DREAMWORLD | 355 toys on the first floor and 293 on the second floor | [   ] |

| Toys and More | 403 toys on the first floor and 396 on the second floor | [   ] |

| ADVENTURELAND | 320 toys on the first floor and 490 on the second floor | [   ] |

688 toys on the first floor and
309 on the second floor

[   ]

718 toys on the first floor and
281 on the second floor

[   ]

Name _____ Date _____

Using knowledge of sums of two odd/even numbers

1 What do you notice about all the numbers the clowns
are holding?

| 3 | 15 | 7 | 9 | 17 | 23 | 5 | 31 | 29 |

What types of numbers are they? ....

| 4 | 12 | 16 | 8 | 2 | 24 | 36 | 42 | 10 |

What types of numbers are these? ....

Add these numbers.

5 + 7 = ☐   7 + 9 = ☐   13 + 5 = ☐   17 + 11 = ☐

What do you notice about all the numbers in the questions?

....

What do you notice about all the numbers in the answers?

....

Try some more of your own.

Add these numbers.

4 + 8 = ☐   10 + 6 = ☐   14 + 12 = ☐   18 + 4 = ☐

What do you notice about all the numbers in the questions?

....

What do you notice about all the numbers in the answers?

....

Try some more of your own.

A | *Masterpieces:* **Addition and Subtraction** CHECKING RESULTS   YEARS 3/4

Name _____ Date _____

Using knowledge of sums of odd/even numbers

1 Write 5 even numbers ....
  Write 5 odd numbers ....

---

2 Add an odd and an even number in each box like this:

| 3 + 8 = 11 | | | | |

  Put a ring around the correct answer: odd + even = odd **or** even

---

3 Add an even and an odd number in each box.

◯ ◯ ◯ ◯ ◯

  Put a ring around the correct answer: even + odd = odd **or** even

---

4 What happens when we add 3 odd numbers?
  Put a ring around the correct answer:
        odd + odd + odd = odd **or** even

5 What happens when we add 3 even numbers?
  Put a ring around the correct answer:
        even + even + even = odd **or** even

---

6 Use the information above to check these answers.
  Put a cross next to any that are wrong.

17 + 15 = 32   51 + 85 = 136   5 + 17 + 89 = 112

28 + 42 = 70   49 + 262 = 310   6 + 18 + 768 = 792

62 + 57 = 120   122 + 188 = 409   14 + 626 + 50 = 690

Name _____ Date _____

Using knowledge of sums and differences of odd/even numbers

1 Put a ring around the correct answer.

odd + odd = odd **or** even

even + even = odd **or** even

odd + even = odd **or** even

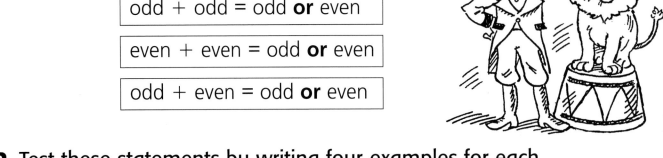

2 Test these statements by writing four examples for each.
Put a ring around the correct answer.

odd − odd = odd **or** even

even − even = odd **or** even

odd − even = odd **or** even

even − odd = odd **or** even

3 Use the information above to check these answers.
Put a cross next to any that are wrong.

87 + 15 = 103	54 + 88 = 141	217 + 538 = 755
153 − 47 = 105	408 − 262 = 146	891 − 768 = 123
672 − 57 = 615	520 − 188 = 332	551 − 287 = 263

Masterpieces Ginn & Company 1999. Copying permitted for purchasing school only. This material is not copyright free.

Answers

Page 4 – Diagnostic assessment

1 9   14   14
   5   6   11

2 100   65   15

3 700   400

4 20   17   22
   8   9   9

5 100   64   28

6 650   450

7 31   31   37
   8   7   5

8 100   71   33

9 600   750

Page 5

1 7   7   9
  14   12   15
   3   5   5
  11   10   8

2 16   4   17   8
  19   10   17   11
  11   10   19   18

Page 6

1 8   10   20   17   19   20
  11   13   15   12   15   16

  18   20   16   20   17   16
  15   17   14   18   15   14

2   7   8   5   6   6   5
  11   18   19   9   14   15   14   20   19
  12   19   20   14   19   20   12   18   17

Page 7

1 20   18   19   18   20   17
  15   13   20   19   19   16

  16   15   9   7   12   9
  18   17   11   20   18   6   18   15
          9   18   16   8   20   17

2   9   7   8   5   8   7
  19   18   20   11   20   18   19   9   14   17   16
  15   14   16   8   17   15   16   12   17   20   19

Page 8

1 5   → 95   10 → 90
  15 → 85   25 → 75
  30 → 70   35 → 65
  40 → 60   50 → 50
  20 → 80   55 → 45

2 35   55   15
  25   60   5

Page 9

1 20 + 80   15 + 85   45 + 55
  52 + 48   64 + 36   56 + 44
  48 + 52   18 + 82   67 + 33

Page 10

1 27 → 73   38 → 62
  58 → 42   64 → 36
  61 → 39

2 63   58
  37
  81   22
  31
  69   92

Page 11

1 700   500
  600   900
  200   100
  400   800
  300   1000

Page 12

1 50 → 950   2 600   800
  100 → 900   700   300
  150 → 850   400   850
  250 → 750
  300 → 700
  350 → 650
  400 → 600
  450 → 550
  500 → 500

Page 13

1 £50 → £950   2 300   650
  £150 → £850   150   250
  £450 → £550   950   550
  £250 → £750   1000   1000
  £350 → £650   350   750

Page 14 – Diagnostic assessment

1	9	25	27
2	6	8	15
3	16	20	20
4	25	21	15
5	67	37	104
6	111	122	116
7	22	25	
8	34	61	18
9	178	2500	2700
10	22	49	74
11	150	150	
12	84	104	18

Page 15

1	40	52
	55	58
	1	6

Page 16

1 341
  65
  77

Page 17

1 add 1
  add 100
  add 1000
  subtract 100
  add 1
  subtract 1000
  add 100
  subtract 10
  add 1000
  add 100
  subtract 1
  add 1000
  add 100
  add 1

Page 18

1 5 6 10 9 8   2 5 13 9 8 12 14

Page 19

1 13
  8
  4
  6
  12
  9
  4
  13
  8
  6

Page 20

8	7
8	8
11	5
12	11
10	8
19	15

Page 21

1	21	41	63
	81	101	102
	121	141	161
	83	122	143

2	19	59	57
	79	99	119
	117	139	159
	137	98	157

Page 22

1	50 + 60	50 + 50 + 10	110
	90 + 80	90 + 90 − 10	170
	70 + 80	70 + 70 + 10	150
	100 + 110	100 + 100 + 10	210
	130 + 120	130 + 130 − 10	250
	150 + 160	150 + 150 + 10	310
	180 + 170	180 + 180 − 10	350
	190 + 180	190 + 190 − 10	370
	250 + 240	250 + 250 − 10	490
	360 + 370	360 + 360 + 10	730

2 510
  850
  890
  950

Page 23

1	49	37	47
	65	89	55
	31	75	93
	71	97	53

2	250	490	710
	330	750	970
	570	870	890
	530	370	950

Page 24

17	15
18	17
17	19
19	19
16	22
24	23
29	33
41	44

Page 25

27	27	32	38	37
42	41	42	35	40
31	32	39	43	57

Page 26

140	150	160
130	190	140
140	190	140
210	170	120
190	180	220

Page 27

49	59
68	78
69	95
99	99
89	74

Page 28

	62
61	101
86	93
120	131
152	137

Page 29

169	169
189	195
196	193
199	200
295	383

Page 30

1

26		28		30	**2**	4		13
	35		38				8	
39		43		46		16		13
	57		62				18	
66		70				16		24
	50						17	
59		68				28		15

Page 31

1

25		41	36	**2**	16		22
	33					18	
55		61			34		27
	41					15	
44		50			17		23
	63					28	
56		45			34		45	57

Page 32

1

45		48	6	**2**	63		42
	58					34	
37		85			109		74
	61					113	31
34		92					
	41						
105		27					
	13						
105		39					
	116						

Page 33

1

15 + 4 = 19	23 + 5 = 28
34 + 3 = 37	42 + 7 = 49
40 + 6 = 46	54 + 5 = 59
29 − 15 = 14	37 − 16 = 21
28 − 12 = 16	34 − 14 = 20
124 + 5 = 129	131 + 8 = 139
148 − 6 = 142	159 − 8 = 151

Page 34

1

121 + 7 = 128	149 − 6 = 143
146 + 8 = 154	131 − 8 = 123
157 + 6 = 163	140 − 7 = 133
100 + 24 = 124	200 − 4 = 196
80 + 27 = 107	300 − 7 = 293
112 + 19 = 131	204 − 9 = 195

Page 35

1

125	162
132	160
136	159
245	228
253	216
269	212
287	600
298	300
310	50
401	330
413	310
426	260

Page 36 – Diagnostic assessment
1 69   89   179

2 121   231   626

3 43

4 181   216   395

5 115   251   479

6 107

7 421   522   732

8 85   38   178

9 183

Page 37
1 92   73   119   119
   85   107   91   117

2 192   161   180   181
   219   229   238   226

Page 38
1 182   191   174
   191   218   285
   416   392   509
   681   729

Page 39
1 331 g   311 g   431 g
   402 g   532 g   504 g
   612 g   631 g   717 g
   900 g   941 g   435 g

Page 40
1 735   255   818
   854 *   254   763
   762   227   845
   846   771   263 591 *

Page 41
1 117   239   449   328
   762   481   683   562
   264   375   658   447
   SHE

Page 42
1 560   53   29
   293   124   489
   375   574   199
   85   153   407
   492   446   71

Page 43
1 70p

2 12

3 27

4 30

5 113

6 £1.20

7 224

8 299

9 95

Page 44
1 65

2 185

3 138

4 73

5 106

6 220

7 227

8 221

9 £4.05

10 403

Page 45
1 £5.52

2 £9.36

3 £3.25

4 £3.36

5 233

6 417

7 a) 188
   b) 89
   c) 106

Page 46 – Diagnostic assessment

1 235 X   295 X

2 3 combinations of 5, 2 and 4, giving 11

3 314 X   312 X

4 3 combinations of 9, 12 and 16, giving 37

5 64 → 60   78 → 80   93 → 90   108 → 110

6 963 X   920 X   56 X   503 X

7 3 combinations of 18, 20 and 21, giving 59

8 195 → 200   238 → 200   449 → 400   670 → 700

Page 47

1 131   241   422
   812   523   727

2 397   279   496
   898   590   853

Page 48

1   498   788
  749   399   560

2 239   250
  215   401

Page 49

1 411→660→−249→411→−174
338→458→−120→338→−165
781→849→−68→781→−253
424→211→+213→424→+162
209→67→+142→209→+340
368→89→+279→368→+275
193→235→+235→358→−193

Page 50

1 15

2 14

3 19

4 16

5 20

6 15

7 18

Page 51

1 18

2 18

3 22

4 23

5 29

6 30

7 32

Page 52

1 28

2 35

3 36

4 150

5 170

6 190

7 190

Page 53

Exact answers:

1 101   110
  150   160
  148   180
  280   477
  266   329

2 28   119
  46   128
  334   326
  443   293
  128   418
  254   137

Page 54

Exact answers:

1 196		**2** 160	
3 307		**4** 412	
5 599		**6** 641	
7 616		**8** 801	
9 749		**10** 797	
11 46		**12** 36	
13 52		**14** 168	
15 104		**16** 295	
17 518		**18** 486	
19 276		**20** 779	

Page 55

Exact answers:

1 502

2 351
398
648
799
810
997   999

Page 56

1 odd numbers
even numbers
12   16   18   28
Numbers in questions are odd.
Numbers in answers are even.
12   16   26   22
Numbers in questions are even.
Numbers in answers are even.

Page 57

1 5 even numbers
5 odd numbers

2 odd + even = odd

3 even + odd = odd

4 odd + odd + odd = odd

5 even + even + even = even

6 5 + 17 + 89 = 112 X
49 + 262 = 310 X
62 + 57 = 120 X   122 + 188 = 409 X

Page 58

1 odd + odd = even
even + even = even
odd + even = odd

2 odd − odd = even
even − even = even
odd − even = odd
even − odd = odd

3 87 + 15 = 103 X   54 + 88 = 141 X
153 − 47 = 105 X
551 − 287 = 263 X